The Golden Age

Painted by the American artist H. WILLARD ORTLIP.
It is in the Hackensack Women's Club, New Jersey

The World of Music

LISTEN AND SING

By

MABELLE GLENN

DIRECTOR OF MUSIC, PUBLIC SCHOOLS, KANSAS CITY, MISSOURI

HELEN S. LEAVITT

INSTRUCTOR IN MUSIC, BOSTON UNIVERSITY AND THE WHEELOCK SCHOOL
BOSTON, MASSACHUSETTS

VICTOR L. F. REBMANN

FORMERLY DIRECTOR OF MUSIC, WESTCHESTER COUNTY, NEW YORK

EARL L. BAKER

FORMERLY DIRECTOR OF PUBLIC SCHOOL MUSIC DEPARTMENT
LAWRENCE COLLEGE, APPLETON, WISCONSIN

ART EDITOR

C. VALENTINE KIRBY

STATE DIRECTOR OF ART EDUCATION, PENNSYLVANIA

GINN AND COMPANY

BOSTON · NEW YORK · CHICAGO · LONDON · ATLANTA · DALLAS · COLUMBUS · SAN FRANCISCO

The World of Music

KINDERGARTEN	ELEMENTARY GRADES	ALL GRADES
SING A SONG	LISTEN AND SING	SINGING DAYS
PLAY A TUNE	TUNING UP	
	RHYTHMS AND RIMES	
	SONGS OF MANY LANDS	
	BLENDING VOICES	
	TUNES AND HARMONIES	

ACKNOWLEDGMENTS

THE EDITORS ARE UNDER DEEP OBLIGATION TO MR. E. W. NEWTON FOR HIS VALUABLE SERVICE, WISE COUNSEL, AND ABLE LEADERSHIP

Acknowledgment is also due to Mr. Ennis D. Davis for assistance in establishing contacts with folk-song collectors in Europe and America; to Mr. Vance Randolph and to the Vanguard Press for permission to use the melodies found on pages 10 and 39, from *Ozark Mountain Folks*; to Frederick A. Stokes Company for the poem "The Busy Postman," reprinted from *All through the Year* by Annette Wynne, copyright 1932 by Annette Wynne; for the poem "The Goldfish," from *Everything and Anything* by Dorothy Aldis, used by permission of the publishers, Minton, Balch and Company; for the poem "Beetles," from *Goose Grass Rhymes* by Monica Shannon, copyright 1930 by Doubleday, Doran and Company, Inc.; for the poem "My Policeman," printed with permission from *The Fairy Green* by Rose Fyleman, copyright 1923 by Doubleday, Doran and Company, Inc.; for the poem "Bobby's Nose," from *In the Wind's Whistle* by Eleanor Jewett, used by permission of the publisher, Ralph Fletcher Seymour. The original illustrations are by Maud and Miska Petersham.

P. 28

Classified Contents

5

Classified Contents

There are here 120 songs, of which 62 are folk songs and 58 are composed songs, which may be taught by rote.

All the songs correlate with the child's studies, interests, and experience.

Reproductions of noted pictures: The Golden Age, *H. Willard Ortlip*, frontispiece; Carnation Lily, Lily, Rose, *John Singer Sargent*, 19; Miss Bowles and Her Dog, *Sir Joshua Reynolds*, 38; A Modern Cinderella, *Jessie Willcox Smith*, 55; Seeing, *Jessie Willcox Smith*, 106; The Holiday, *Edward Henry Potthast*, 123.

Clear September

Edith Robbins
Norwegian Folk Tune

Lightly

1. Clear Sep - tem - ber, cool and bright,
2. Clear Sep - tem - ber laugh - ing, said,

Shin - ing with a gold - en light,
"Leaves come down from o - ver - head,

Said, "I'll paint the leaves at night
Make a bed of gold and red,

With col - ors gay."
Then blow a - way."

9

Fiddle Songs

Louise Kessler

Ozark Mountain Folk Tune

Sprightly

1. Fa - ther takes me on his knee,
2. While his fid - dle sings to me

Plays a fid - dle song for me,
I'm as hap - py as can be;

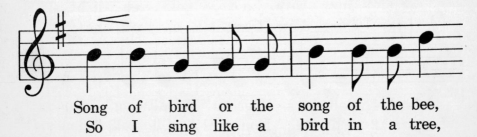

Song of bird or the song of the bee,
So I sing like a bird in a tree,

Or song of the wind a - blow - ing.
A song of the wind a - blow - ing.

Shake Your Boughs

Jane Beecham

Lettish Folk Tune

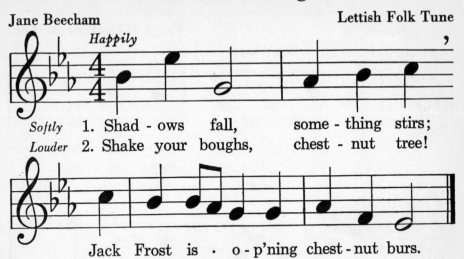

Softly 1. Shad - ows fall, some - thing stirs;
Louder 2. Shake your boughs, chest - nut tree!

Jack Frost is · o - p'ning chest - nut burs.
Drop down some big brown nuts for me.

Hear Me Calling

Elizabeth Garrett

C. D. Daniel

1st Child 1. Call - ing, "Do - ra!" [1] Call - ing, "Do - ra!"
2d Child 2. I'll call, "Don - ald!" I'll call, "Don - ald!"

Ev' - ry morn - ing you can hear me call - ing you!
Ev' - ry morn - ing you can hear me call - ing you!

[1] Other names may be substituted.

Round the Pear Tree

Lois Lenski   Danish Folk Tune

Brightly and lightly

1. Here   we   go   tip - py   toe,
2. Branch - es   low,   here we   go

Danc - ing   round   the   pear   tree;
Climb - ing   up   the   pear   tree;

Pears   may   fall,   catch them   all.
Pears   are   sweet,   good   to   eat.

Did - dle,   dump - ty,   dai - rie!
Did - dle,   dump - ty,   dai - rie!

Little Ducky Duddle

Moiselle Renstrom

Moiselle Renstrom

Playfully

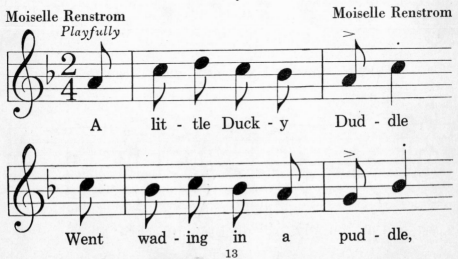

A lit - tle Duck - y Dud - dle

Went wad - ing in a pud - dle,

13

Went wad-ing in a pud-dle quite small. .

Said he, "It does-n't mat-ter

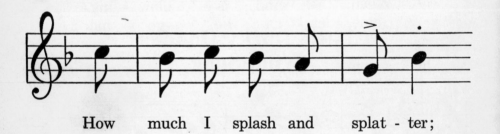

How much I splash and splat-ter;

I'm on-ly a duck-y aft-er all." .

A Walk in the Woods

Marjorie Knapp

Ukrainian Folk Tune

In steady rhythm

1. Through the woods we   shall go walk - ing
2. There we'll hear the   squir - rels talk - ing,
3. All   the leaves will   chat - ter, chat - ter,
4. While the nuts go   pat - ter, pat - ter,

When the leaves are   fall - ing.
Hear the blue jays   call - ing.
When the wind is   blow - ing.
Come, let us be   go - ing.

Wind Song

Virginia Lynd Hartley

Ethel L. Higgins

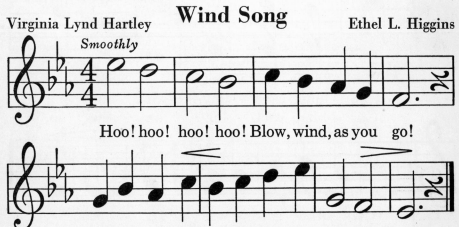

Smoothly

Hoo! hoo! hoo! hoo! Blow, wind, as you go!

You may bring the rain or bring the soft, white snow.

The Turkey and the Hen

Maud W. Niedermeyer

Danish Folk Tune

With animation

2d Choir 1. "Gob - ble," said the tur - key;
2. "Gob - ble," said the tur - key;

1st Choir "Cack - le," said the hen. . .
"Cack - le," said the hen. . .

Off they start - ed on the run,
Off they go to have some fun,

Gob - bling, cack - ling, all in fun,
Gob - bling, cack - ling, on the run,

2d Choir When the gate was o - pen.
For the gate is o - pen.

Swinging in the Willow

Kate Forman

English Folk Tune

Gracefully and not too fast

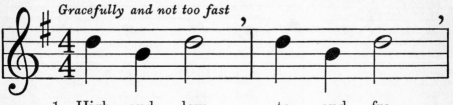

1. High and low, to and fro,
2. When I'm high in the sky

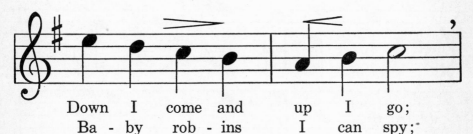

Down I come and up I go;
Ba - by rob - ins I can spy;

Friend - ly wil - low tree, when I swing up high,
All the lit - tle birds wink and blink at me,

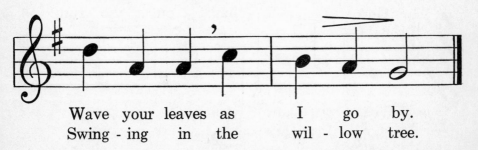

Wave your leaves as I go by.
Swing - ing in the wil - low tree.

In the Garden

Marjorie Knapp

Henry P. Cross

Sweetly and smoothly

1. Lil - ies in the gar - den stand;
2. Chil - dren in the gar - den play

Cool and white they're grow - ing.
With the blos - soms grow - ing;

Pink or red on ei - ther hand,
Gold - en - haired and fair are they,

A tall car - na - tion blow - ing.
And red their cheeks are glow - ing.

Carnation Lily, Lily, Rose

Painted by the American artist JOHN SINGER SARGENT.
The picture is now in the Tate Gallery, London

Dancing Leaves

Susanna Myers

Italian Folk Tune

1. When the au - tumn wind is blow-ing
   All the leaves go fly - ing, danc-ing;
2. When a gen - tle breeze is blow-ing
   All the ti - ny leaves go danc-ing

On a clear Oc - to - ber day.
Trees will soon be bare and gray.
On a sun - ny A - pril day.
Just as though they loved to play.

Jack, Be Nimble

Mother Goose

Lolia M. Littlehales

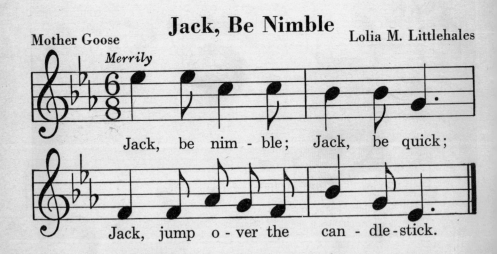

Jack, be nim - ble; Jack, be quick;

Jack, jump o - ver the can - dle-stick.

Climbing

Marchette Gaylord Chute   Carinthian Folk Tune

Lightly and sprightly

I am climb - ing up the moun-tain,

Go - ing high - er, ev - er high - er.

Soon, if I try, I can reach the sky;

But I don't think I'll try.

1

My Bunny

Virginia Lynd Hartley

Irish Folk Tune

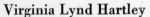

Lightly

1. I   keep   my rab - bit   in   his house,
2. His   nose can wig - gle   ev - 'ry way;

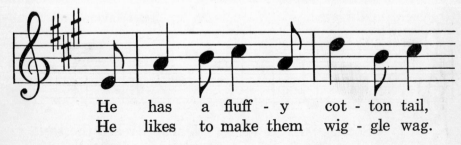

But   let   him out when it's   sun - ny.
His   silk - y ears are   so   fun - ny;

He   has   a fluff - y   cot - ton tail,
He   likes to make them   wig - gle wag.

And   I would-n't sell him for   mon - ey.
My   dear lit - tle, queer lit - tle   bun - ny.

Dinkey Donkey

Mary Smith

French Melody

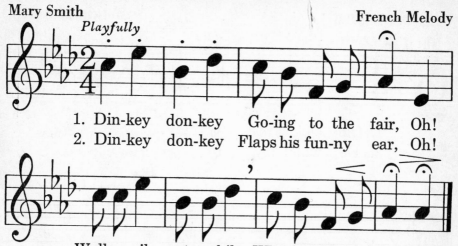

1. Din-key don-key Go-ing to the fair, Oh!
2. Din-key don-key Flaps his fun-ny ear, Oh!

Walk a mile, rest a while: When will he be there? Oh!
Walk a mile, rest a while: It will take a year, Oh!

Pony

Gretchen O. Murray

Yugoslavian Folk Tune

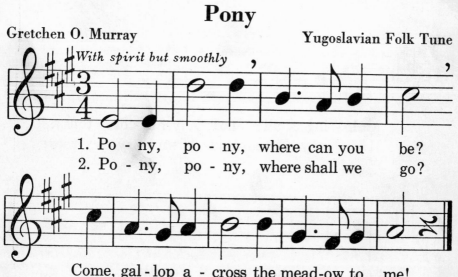

1. Po - ny, po - ny, where can you be?
2. Po - ny, po - ny, where shall we go?

Come, gal - lop a - cross the mead-ow to me!
We nev - er will tell, and no one will know.

Old Jack Frost

Moiselle Renstrom

Moiselle Renstrom

Happily

1. Old Jack Frost is out to - day,
2. He will try to pinch each nose;

Hoo - - - - oo - - - - - - - - - oo.
Hoo - - - - oo - - - - - - - - oo.

Mak - ing all the chil - dren say,
He may bite and sting your toes;

"Oh, oh, oh!"
Oh, oh, oh!

Song of Autumn

Kathleen Malone

Hungarian Folk Tune

Au - tumn winds are call - ing,

Col - ored leaves are fall - ing;

Dressed for au - tumn weath - er

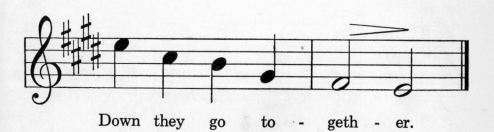

Down they go to - geth - er.

The Echo

Fanny Giralda Pheatt   Fanny Giralda Pheatt

2D CHOIR "Whoo - oo, whoo - oo," you   call;

1ST CHOIR And   then   an   an - swer   small

Comes   back   to   you,   as   if   it   knew,

ALL   "Whoo - oo,   whoo - oo,   whoo - oo!"   .

Froggie

Maud W. Niedermeyer

Norwegian Folk Tune

Lively

1. Frog - gie slept up - on a stone,
   Mis - ter Hawk said, "Ha, ha, ha!
2. Frog - gie o - pened wide her eyes;
   Then she jumped with one big croak

While the sun was shin - ing.
Now I can be din - ing."
No one yet had caught her:
Right in - to the wa - ter.

The Flag

Elizabeth Garrett

Swedish Folk Tune

With spirit

1. All sa - lute the flag that is wav - ing,
2. One and all we pledge our al - le - giance

Wav - ing proud - ly a - gainst the sky.
To our flag as it pass - es by.

My Policeman

Rose Fyleman

Newton Swift

With spirit

1. He   is   al - ways   stand - ing   there
2. All   the cars   and   tax - is   do
3. Though   I   seem   so   ver - y   small,

At   the cor - ner   of   the Square;
Ev - 'ry - thing   he   tells them   to,
I   am not   a -   fraid   at   all;

He   is ver - y   big   and fine,
And   the lit - tle   er - rand boys
He   and I   are   friends, you   see,

And his   sil - ver   but - tons   shine.
When they   pass him   make   no   noise.
And he   al - ways smiles   at   me.

Bobby's Nose

Eleanor Jewett

Frederic Daly

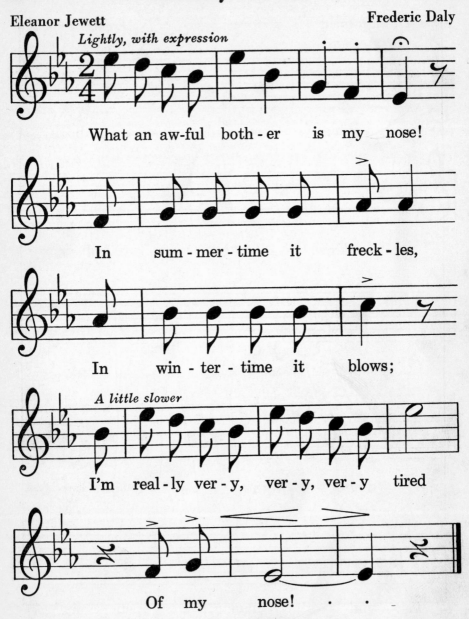

What an aw-ful both-er is my nose!

In sum-mer-time it freck-les,

In win-ter-time it blows;

I'm real-ly ver-y, ver-y, ver-y tired

Of my nose!

My Pocketbook

Ethel Crowninshield

English Folk Tune

1ST CHILD "You've lost your pock - et - book?

Dear! dear! dear! And now you feel ver - y

sad, I fear." 2D CHILD "Oh, no! no! no! it

does-n't mat-ter an - y; 'Twas all worn out and

did - n't have a pen - ny."

Halloween

Susanna Myers

Lettish Folk Tune

With spirit but smoothly

1. Jack - o' - lan - tern   burns his   can - dle
2. Owls   up - on   the   wav - ing   tree - tops

Bright   through the wind - y   night;
Hoot   through the wind - y   night;

Witch - es   on   their   broom - sticks ride
Brown - ies   dance   on   Hal - low - een

By   the   Jack - o' - lan - tern   light.
By   the   Jack - o' - lan - tern   light.

My Gingerbread Man

Mildred Adair

Mildred Adair

Cur - rants for his but - tons,

A rai - sin for his nose;

My man is made of gin - ger - bread

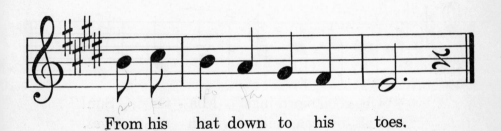

From his hat down to his toes.

Morning and Night

Maud W. Niedermeyer

Czech Folk Tune

Brightly 1. When the morn-ing light is near,
Softly   2. When at night I go to bed,

When the morn-ing sounds I hear,
When "good nights" have all been said,

Up I jump and out I run:
I go sail-ing through the skies

"Oh, good morn-ing, Mis-ter Sun!"
Just by clos-ing both my eyes.

Two Gardens

Susanna Myers

German Folk Tune

With expression

1. Grow - ing   in   my   gar - den
2. In   my   oth - er   gar - den

Are   bright yel - low pan - sies,   row aft - er row;
Are   beans and po - ta - toes,   row aft - er row;

Man - y,   man - y   blos - soms
Peas   and   corn   and   car - rots,

Be - cause   I   weed   and   hoe.
Be - cause   I   weed   and   hoe.

Good Morning

Marjorie Carol   Ludwig van Beethoven

Smoothly and sweetly

1. Up   in   a   tree - top,
2. Down   by   the   riv - er

A   blue   bird   has   her   nest.   ·
A   vio - let   has   her   home,   ·

When   breez - es   blow   soft - ly
She   looks   in   the   wa - ter

A little slower

We   hear   her   sing, "Good morn-ing."   ·
That   laughs and sings, "Good morn-ing."   ·

The Wind

Lolia M. Littlehales   Lolia M. Littlehales

Brightly but not too fast

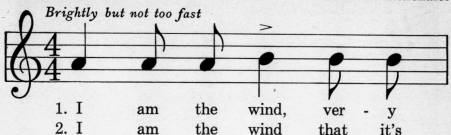

1. I   am   the   wind,   ver - y
2. I   am   the   wind   that   it's

strong and bold;   I   make you   shiv - er when the
fun   to   know, The warm spring wind that makes the

weath - er   is   cold.   We   may have snow;
pret - ty flow'rs grow.   Gone   is   the   snow;

hear the wind blow,   Hoo - - oo - - - oo!
hear the wind blow,   Hoo - - oo - - - oo!

1

Miss Bowles and Her Dog

Painted by the English artist SIR JOSHUA REYNOLDS,
in 1776. It is now in the Wallace Collection, London

My Dog

Marjorie Knapp   Ozark Mountain Folk Tune

Joyously

1. Old Rov-er knows when I   go a - way,
2. You nev-er saw an - y dog so   fine,

Looks at my   hat and   tries to   say,
Big shag-gy   tail and   eyes that   shine;

"Please let me   run! You will have a lot of
He's proud that he   al-ways has be-longed to

fun   If you'll take me with you to   play."
me;   I'm proud when I think he is   mine.

1

The Birthday Party

Fay Wilson

Austrian Folk Tune

1st Child 1. "Will you come to   see my broth-er and   me?

2. "On my cake there'll be six can-dles for   me,

I'm six years old and the par-ty's at   three."

I'll blow them out in just one blow, you'll see!"

2d Child   "Oh, yes, I'll be   there, all dressed up with care;

"I've some-thing for   you, all tied up with blue;

I'll wear my new shoes and a   bow in my hair."

I like it so much I hope you'll like it too."

40

The Bullfrog

Elizabeth C. Taylor   Mary B. Black

1. A bull-frog in a clean white vest
2. The bull-frog could not sing a note;

Lived in the place he liked the best,
He had no mu-sic in his throat.

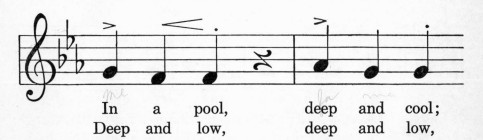

In a pool, deep and cool;
Deep and low, deep and low,

He liked the wa-ter cool.
His voice was ver-y low.

Wooden Shoes

Mary Smith

Robert W. Gibb

1. Who is mak-ing all that noise? Click, clack, click, clack!
2. Jan[1] will walk a-long so fast: Tap, tap, tap, tap!

See, it is Dutch girls and boys: Click, clack, click, clack!
Min-na's slow and al-ways last: Tap, tap, tap, tap!

Walk - ing round in shoes of wood,
Leave their shoes out - side the door,

Mak - ing them go where they should;
Walk in stock - ings on the floor;

[1] Pronounced "Yahn."

Wooden Shoes (*Continued*)

Very softly

I would do it if I could: Click, clack, click, clack!
Qui - et now, they click no more: Tap, tap, tap, tap.

Bunny Bun

Mary Smith French Folk Tune

1. A   bun - ny rab - bit   hop - ping by,
2. The   boy then said   to   Bun - ny Bun,

With fluff - y tail and a   smile in his eye,
"Please stay a - while and we'll play and have fun.

Said to   a   boy   he   met by the way,
O Bun - ny Bun, don't hur - ry   a - way;

"I'm glad   to see you this beau - ti - ful day."
I'm glad you're here on this beau - ti - ful day."

Tinka and the Sparrows

After the original by
Marchette Gaylord Chute

Russian Folk Song

Tink - a's   tree   is   full   of   cher - ries;

Tink - a's   bush   is   full   of   ber - ries.

When the spar - rows   come for their din - ner

Tink - a makes them   all   fly   a - way.

Mother Dear

Susanna Myers   Hungarian Folk Tune

1. Moth-er, I am sing - ing songs for you;
2. When you see me smil - ing, Moth-er dear,

Lit - tle songs I make for you
You will know the mean - ing true

To show the love I have for you,
Of hap - py songs I make for you,

I have for you.
O Moth - er dear.

Little Turtle

Elizabeth Garrett

Lettish Folk Tune

1. Lit - tle tur - tle,   lit - tle tur - tle,
2. When the sun's no   long - er shin - ing,

For   a   house he'll   nev - er   lack;
When the   rain - drops   gen - tly   fall,

Far   a - way though   he may trav - el,
He's   no   need   for   an um - brel - la;

Tur - tle's house   is   on   his back.
He   will   not   get   wet   at   all.

Shopping

Laura E. Richards   Robert W. Gibb

Gracefully

1st Child 1. "Good Mis-ter   Gro - cer,   O,   sir!
          2. "Good Mis-ter   Gro - cer,   O,   sir!
          3. "Good Mis-ter   Gro - cer,   O,   sir!

What   do   you   have   to   show,   sir?"
They're not   for   me,   you   know,   sir!
Real - ly you're rath - er   slow,   sir.

2d Child "I've   pick - les   and   crack - ers
          A   grape   or   a   cher - ry
          If   you'll give me   an - y

And   smick - ers and   smack - ers
Would   make   me   so   mer - ry
To   match with my   pen - ny

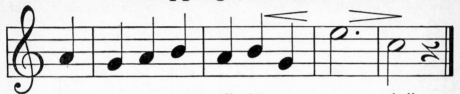

And   saus-ag - es   all   in   a   row,   sir."
That   joy - ful - ly   off   I would   go,   sir."
Please   hur - ry   a - way   on your   toe,   sir."

Mister Owl

Mildred Adair   Mildred Adair

Smoothly

1ST CHOIR   O,   Mis - ter   Owl, you   look   so   wise!

2D CHOIR   Too - whoo,   too - whoo!

1ST CHOIR   You   have   such   ver - y   fun - ny   eyes.

2D CHOIR   Too - whoo,   too - whoo!

19593

Sailing

Mildred Adair   Mildred Adair

With tenderness

1ST CHOIR

1. I like to watch the clouds go by,
2. O - ver the world I'd like to fly,

2D CHOIR

Sail - ing by, sail - ing by.
Like to fly, like to fly,

1ST CHOIR

I'd like to trav - el through the sky,
Driv-ing an air - plane through the sky,

2D CHOIR

'Way up high! . .
'Way up high! . .

My Playhouse

Susanna Myers

Russian Folk Tune

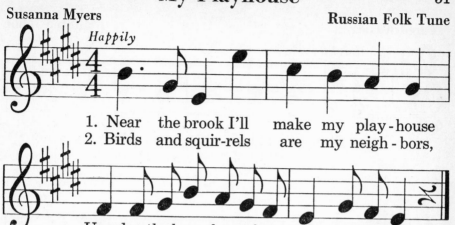

Happily

1. Near the brook I'll make my play-house
2. Birds and squir-rels are my neigh-bors,

Un-der the branch-es of a green ma-ple tree.
Snug in their hous-es up a-bove, o-ver me.

Traffic Lights

Elizabeth Garrett

Robert W. Gibb

Stop lights on the cor - ner,

Stop lights, red and green;

You can al - ways cross in safe - ty

If you know just what they mean.

Our Store

Kathleen Malone

Russian Folk Tune

1. Dur - ing rain - y weath - er   we   get to - geth - er
2. There we sell po - ta - toes, round red to - ma - toes,

In   the   house where we   all   play   store;
Clocks and   shoes and some bears that   roar;

There   is   no   tell - ing   what we'll be   sell - ing
All   kinds of   ber - ries,   large juic - y   cher - ries,

Till   the   weath - er   is   clear   once   more.
Just   as   long   as   the   rain - drops   pour.

A Modern Cinderella

Jane Beecham Mary B. Black

1. Can this be Cin - der - el - la here?
2. Hold up your foot! Yes, it is plain

And we thought we nev - er should find you; ·
They be - long to you and no oth - er; ·

You ran a - way so fast, my dear,
Now you can go out in the rain,

That you left your rub - bers be - hind you. ·
And run safe - ly home to your moth - er. ·

A Modern Cinderella

Reproduced by permission, from the painting
by the American artist JESSIE WILLCOX SMITH

Five Little Drums

Annette Wynne

Hungarian Folk Tune

1. Five lit - tle drums beat one, two, three!
2. Five lit - tle drums. Oh, my, what fun!

See, we are step - ping bold and free!
Is - n't it good that work is done?

Cheer-i - ly we march this sun - ny day.
Keep-ing step to - geth - er: one, two, three.

Rub - a - dub-dub, dub - dub, all the way.
Rub - a - dub-dub, dub - dub, come with me!

A Birthday

Susanna Myers   Belgian Folk Tune

Happily

Ma - ry, we wish you a   hap - py birth - day;

Is - n't it nice that to - day is your birth-day!

When the good fair - ies make wish - es come true,

May they bring won-der-ful   things to you.

1

Mister Turkey

L. E. Ashley

Robert W. Gibb

With spirit

See him strut - ting all a - round,

Fat Mis - ter Tur - key!

Hear the gob - ble, gob - ble sound,

Fat Mis - ter Tur - key!

He eats all the food we bring,

Yel - low corn and ev - 'ry - thing.

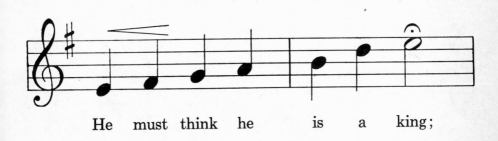

He must think he is a king;

In time

Proud Mis - ter Tur - key!

Thanksgiving Day

Mildred Adair   Mildred Adair

Thanks-giv-ing Day is near.   I'm thank-ful, are you? Thanks-giv-ing Day is near. I'm thank-ful, are you? For songs and games and sun-shine, I'm thank-ful, are you? For fa-ther and for moth-er, I'm thank-ful, are you?

The Fairy

Alice G. Thorn

Welsh Folk Tune

Gracefully and smoothly

Oh, there once was a fair-y, a ti-ny wee thing; By the light of the moon she would dance and would sing. When the day first be-gan and the sun was not up, She would fly home to sleep in a bright but-ter-cup.

Market Day in Town

Mary Root Kern   Mary Root Kern

Merrily

1. I saw my fa - ther ride a - way,
2. Oh, some-thing nice he'll bring to us,
3. If all we wish he'd bring us back,

Gal - lop - ing up, gal - lop - ing down;
Gal - lop - ing up, gal - lop - ing down.
Gal - lop - ing up, gal - lop - ing down,

He waved his hand as if to say,
Oh, some-thing nice he'll bring to us
His sad - dle - bag would sure - ly crack,

"I'm rid - ing off to town."
From mar - ket day in town.
A - rid - ing home from town.

Shadow Play

Carol Fuller

Wolfgang Amadeus Mozart

1. How I like to watch my shad - ow,
2. I am not a - fraid at bed - time,

Play - ing games with me all day!
Though my shad - ow play is through;

When I run,[1] it runs a - long be-side,
For the night, with all its pret - ty stars,

And al - ways goes my way.
Is one big shad - ow too.

[1] Jump, hop, walk.

Kites

Mary E. Shield

Carinthian Folk Tune

In well-marked rhythm

1. Will   you   come   out   to - day?
2. We'll   hur - ry,   you   and   I;

Rain   clouds   have   blown   a - way!
For   while   the   wind   is   high

I   know   what   we   will   play;
Our   kites   we'll   gay - ly   fly

It's   lots   of   fun.
Out   in   the   sun.

Little Pigs

Beatrice Wadhams

Slavic Folk Tune

Black and white are my three lit-tle pigs,

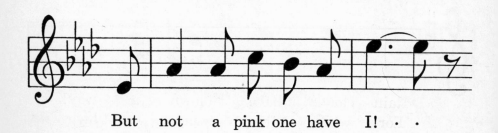

But not a pink one have I! · ·

They'll run to me when I call, "Wee-wee!"

I'll feed them by and by. · ·

The Skaters

Laura E. Richards

Swiss Folk Tune

1. Flash - ing, dash - ing   to   and   fro,
2. Up   and   down   and   here   and   there,

See   the   mer - ry   skat - ers   go!
Hands a - cross   to   make   a   pair.

Skies   are   clear,   the   sun   is   bright;
Eyes   a - spar - kle,   cheeks   a - glow;

Skat - ing   is   the   heart's   de - light.
Mer - ry   skat - ing   makes   them   so.

A Little Boy

Mary Smith

English Folk Tune

Gracefully and lightly

1. A lit - tle boy once said to me,
2. A lit - tle girl once said to me,

"I'll tell you what I'd like to be:
"I'll tell you what I'd like to be:

A butch - er, a bak - er, a can - dy - man,
A mak - er of dress - es for you and Nan,

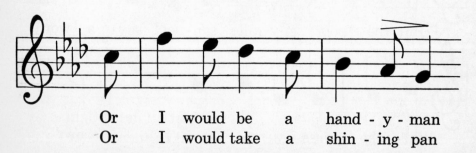

Or I would be a hand - y - man
Or I would take a shin - ing pan

And wa-ter the gar-den for 'Liz-a-beth Ann."
And bake man-y cook-ies for 'Liz-a-beth Ann."

The Poor Giraffe

Marion W. Flexner   Dorothy P. Clark

Playfully

Oh, the frog can croak, and the horse can neigh,

And the pup-py dog says, "Bow-wow-wow-wow";

But the poor gi-raffe can-not say a word,

While the puss-y cat says, "Me-ow."

Farm Music

Carol Fuller

Danish Folk Tune

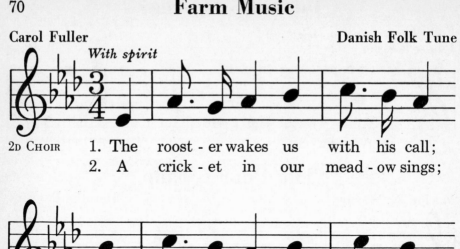

With spirit

2D Choir

1. The roost - er wakes us with his call;
2. A crick - et in our mead - ow sings;

Our pret - ty doves are coo - ing;
The puss - y cat is purr - ing,

1ST Choir The boss - y calf is new and small,
While like a bird with snow - y wings

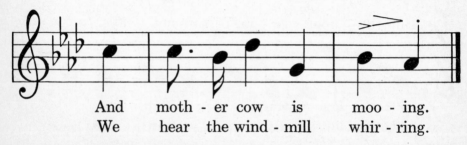

And moth - er cow is moo - ing.
We hear the wind - mill whir - ring.

Dancing Together

English version by
Louise Kessler

Norwegian Folk Song

With well-marked rhythm

1. Put your right hand for-ward, clap! clap!
2. Put your right foot for-ward, tap! tap!

Left   hand,   then   a   clap!   clap!
Left   foot,   then   a   tap!   tap!

Round we are swing-ing, our voic-es sing-ing,
Round we are swing-ing, our voic-es sing-ing,

Danc - ing   with   a   clap!   clap!
Danc - ing   with   a   tap!   tap!

On a Rainy Day

Josephine Royle

John P. Sacco

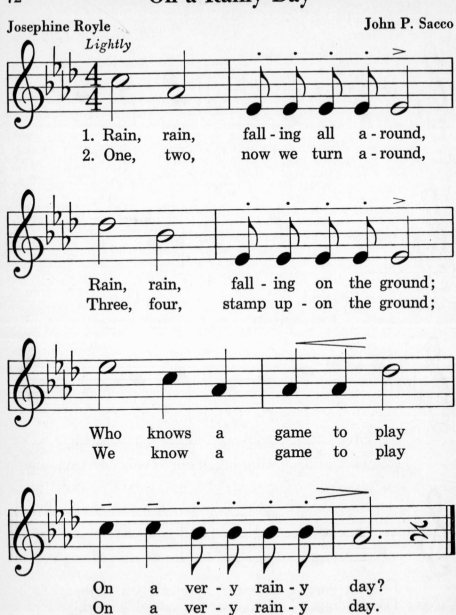

Lightly

1. Rain, rain, fall - ing all a - round,
2. One, two, now we turn a - round,

Rain, rain, fall - ing on the ground;
Three, four, stamp up - on the ground;

Who knows a game to play
We know a game to play

On a ver - y rain - y day?
On a ver - y rain - y day.

Chickadee

Mary Smith

Bohemian-Czech Folk Tune

Brightly

1. Sing   for   me,   chick - a - dee!
2. Sing   for   me,   chick - a - dee!

Lit - tle   bird   a - way   up   in the tree.
Lit - tle   bird   a - way   up   in the tree.

Sing   for   me,   chick - a - dee!
Sing   for   me,   chick - a - dee!

Fun - ny   lit - tle   chick - a - dee.
I'll   sing, too, with   chick - a - dee.

1

Horseback Riding

Susanna Myers

Swedish Folk Tune

Playfully

1. Let us play a game of a
2. Down the wind - ing road we will
3. When we reach the hills and the
4. Here we are at home, you must

boy and his po - ny; I will be the
trot - trot - a - trot - trot, Man - y, man - y
road's rough and ston - y, I will let you
eat in your sta - ble; There's the sup - per

boy and you be the po - ny.
miles trot - trot - trot - a - trot - trot.
walk, my good lit - tle po - ny.
bell, I'll eat at the ta - ble.

Little Bird

Mary Smith

Welsh Folk Tune

Lit - tle bird, sing to me a sto - ry!

Tell me where you have been to - day.

Can you sing to me a - bout the chil - dren

You have talked to a - long the way?

A Thousand Stars

Ethel Crowninshield   Robert Schumann

Softly and slowly

1. A thou-sand stars up in the sky,
2. The day is light, the night is dark,

Just one shin - ing sun;
But God nev - er sleeps.

So man - y chil - dren , in the world,
And o - ver chil - dren ev - 'ry - where

Yet God knows ev - 'ry one.
A lov - ing watch He keeps.

Annette Wynne
Adapted

Austrian Folk Tune

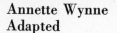

Cheerfully and sprightly

1. The bus - y post - man whis - tles
2. He likes to see us hap - py,

Be - cause he's glad to bring
So car - ries ev - 'ry day

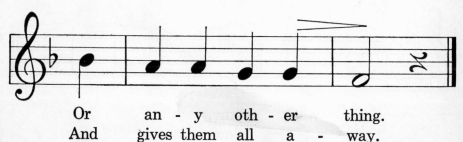

A let - ter or a val - en - tine
The mag - a - zines and let - ters too,

Or an - y oth - er thing.
And gives them all a - way.

Pets

Ethel H. Tewksbury

R. T. Bjorkman

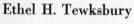

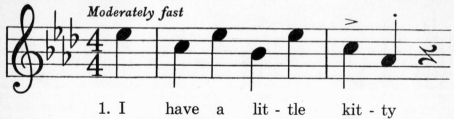

1. I   have a lit - tle kit - ty
2. I   have a wool - ly dog - gy,

With   nice   warm   fur,
And   he   knows   how

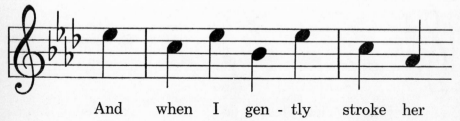

And   when I gen - tly stroke her
To   say, "I thank you kind - ly."

She will   purr, purr,   purr.
It   is   bow - wow - wow.

Shadows

Nancy Byrd Turner

Swedish Folk Tune

1. On a moon-beam shin - ing bright - ly,
2. One's a fair - y, one's a brown - ie,

Up and down and ver - y light - ly,
Up and up, then down, down, down - y.

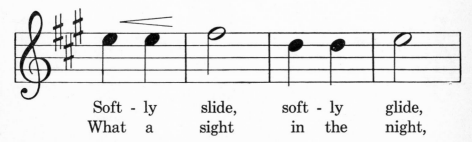

Soft - ly slide, soft - ly glide,
What a sight in the night,

Shad - ows laugh - ing as they ride.
Coast - ing on a beam of light!

Three Dukes

American Traditional   American Traditional

1.   Here come three dukes a - rid - ing,   rid - ing,
2. "What are you rid-ing here for, here for,

rid - ing. Here come three dukes a - rid - ing,
here for? What are you rid - ing here for?"

Ran - son, pran - son,   tan - tan - ta - ra!
Ran - son, pran - son,   tan - tan - ta - ra!

3. "We're riding here to marry,
    Marry, marry," etc.

4. "Now which one will you choose, sir?
    Choose, sir, choose, sir?" etc.

5. "I think that I'll take this one,
    This one, this one," etc.

Let Us Be Merry

Hope Ann Rhodes

Polish Carol

Lis - ten to our mer - ry, mer - ry song!

Peace and joy to Christ-mas day be - long;

Through all the world go Christ-mas car-ols ring - ing,

Through all the world go hap-py chil-dren sing-ing!

Christmas Time

Ethel Crowninshield   Ethel Crowninshield

Brightly

1. I like the Christ - mas time
2. Moth - er will hang a wreath

For lots of dif - f'rent things;
Of hol - ly on our door,

I like the Christ - mas songs
As she has done each year

That ev - 'ry - bod - y sings.
At Christ-mas time be - fore.

I like the Christ - mas trees
Then on the win - dow sill

In shops a - long the way;   I like the
Some can-dles there will be,   Shin-ing on

best of all The things we give a - way.
Christ-mas Eve For ev - 'ry - one to see.

Last Night

Maud W. Niedermeyer   Lettish Folk Tune

Softly

Last night the snow fell soft as wool

And it left the trees all beau - ti - ful.

Christmas Morning

Marion W. Flexner

Dorothy P. Clark

On Christ-mas day in one of my socks

I found a ti - ny mu - sic box;

I turned the han - dle; to my de - light

It played the car - ol of "Christ-mas Night."

Light, Light Our Candle

English version by
Carol Fuller

French Folk Song

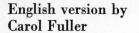

Light, light our can-dle! Let it glow!

Oh, oh, some-one in the snow!

Look, the way is clear, Lit-tle child so dear!

En-ter, Christ-mas Ba-by, we are wait-ing here.

The Toy Shop

Mary Jason

Mabel Caroline Bjornstad

Lightly and happily

1. Let's run to the store where they sell the fine toys
2. The coun-ters are full of a num-ber of things:

For all of the girls and for all of the boys;
A house that has cur-tains and door-bell that rings;

Some dolls that walk and en-gines that run,
Some skates that roll, a ham-mer and nails,

And books full of pic-tures and clowns full of fun.
A box full of mar-bles, and boats that have sails.

A Jolly Little Man

Lolia M. Littlehales   Lolia M. Littlehales

Merrily

There's a   jol - ly   lit - tle   man,

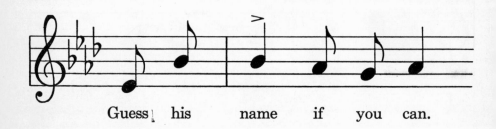

Guess   his   name   if   you   can.

He   has   eyes   shin - ing bright;

He   will   come   on Christ - mas night;

And   he   car - ries   on   his   back

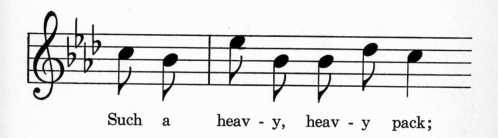

Such   a   heav - y,   heav - y   pack;

He   has   man - y   pres - ents   in   it

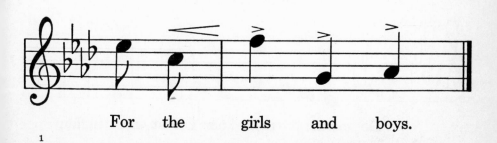

For   the   girls   and   boys.

Two Blackbirds

Mother Goose

G. A. Grant-Schaefer

Once there were two black-birds sit-ting on a

hill, The one named Jack, The oth-er named

Jill! Fly a-way, Jack! Fly away, Jill!

Come a-gain, Jack! Come a-gain, Jill!

The Moon

Eliza Follen

Newton Swift

Oh, look at the moon! She is shin-ing up there;

The Moon (*Continued*)

See, Moth-er! She looks like a lamp in the air.

Last week she was small-er and shaped like a bow;

But now she has grown big-ger and round as an O.

Snowflakes

Gretchen O. Murray

Bohemian Folk Tune

1st Choir 1. Snow - flakes, lit - tle snow - flakes,
All 2. Sleigh - bells now are ring - ing,

I like you, lit - tle snow - flakes;
There's laugh - ing and there's sing - ing;

2d Choir I'll catch you, lit - tle snow - flakes,
Oh, win - ter time is bring - ing

A - danc - ing in the sky.
Such fun as days go by.

Setting the Table

Mary C. Gleitz

Lettish Folk Tune

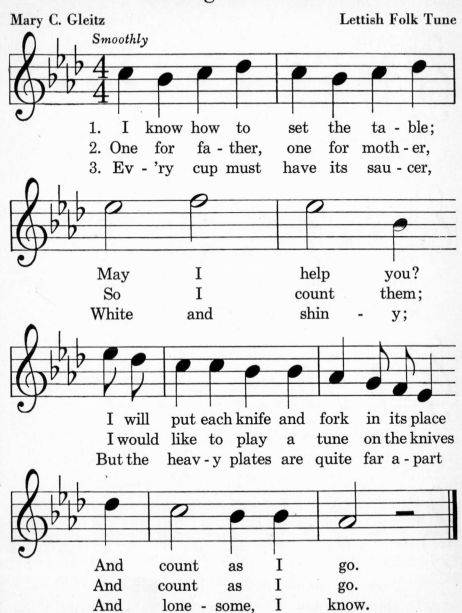

Smoothly

1. I know how to set the ta - ble;
2. One for fa - ther, one for moth - er,
3. Ev - 'ry cup must have its sau - cer,

May I help you?
So I count them;
White and shin - y;

I will put each knife and fork in its place
I would like to play a tune on the knives
But the heav - y plates are quite far a - part

And count as I go.
And count as I go.
And lone - some, I know.

Song For a Rainy Day

Cecil Cowdrey

German Folk Tune

1ST CHOIR 1. Rain-ing, rain-ing, rain - ing   all   day long,
         2. All the frogs are croak - ing,   skies are black,

Not a bird to start a   sin - gle   song;
All the ducks are say - ing, "Quack, quack, quack."

2D CHOIR Drip-ping down so wet from   ev - 'ry tree,
          Rain-ing, rain - ing, rain - ing! Please ex - plain

There is too much rain, it   seems to   me.
How there can be so much   rain, rain, rain!

The Squirrel

Helen Call

Mary Root Kern

A gray lit - tle squir-rel has come to our tree,

He runs all a-round it, so bus - y is he;

But when I bring wal-nuts he quick - ly will see

What ver - y good friends we are go-ing to be.

The Steam Engine

Louise Ayres Garnett

German Folk Tune

1. Choo, choo, choo! Oh, see how we
2. Choo, choo, choo! The wind flies a -

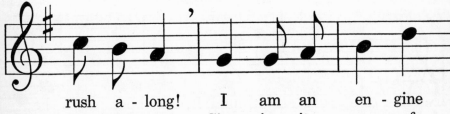

rush a - long! I am an en - gine
long with me, Sing - ing its song of

with a bus - y crew. Hear the bells at
hoo - ry, hoo - ry, hoo. So much noise we're

cross - ings ring ding - a - ding - a - dong!
mak - ing, puff - ing and blow-ing free,

I sing choo, choo, choo, choo, choo, choo!
Sing-ing choo, choo, choo, choo, choo, choo!

Fairy Echoes

Carol Fuller   Austrian Folk Tune

Fair-ies go rid-ing a - round on their but-ter-flies,

Fol-low their Fair - y King, hear-ing at morn

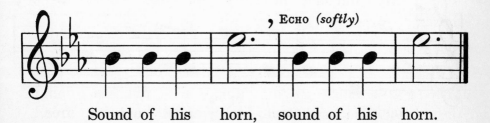

Sound of his horn, sound of his horn.

The Goldfish

Dorothy Aldis

Newton Swift

Playfully

My dar-ling lit-tle · gold-fish has-n't an-y

toes; He swims a-round with-out a sound

And · bumps his hun - gry nose.

A little faster

He can't get out to · play with me,

Nor I get in to him,

Al - though I say, "Come out and play,"

And he, "Come in and swim."

The Lion

G. A. Grant-Schaefer   G. A. Grant-Schaefer

With spirit

Oh, the   li - on has   a   ver - y bush - y

mane, bush - y mane,   And a mouth so ver - y

big, and oh,   so   wide, oh,   so   wide!

You would   be   sur-prised to   see   him yawn

Be - cause there seems to   be   Room for

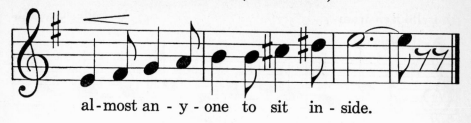

al-most an - y - one to sit in - side.

Fun in Winter

Moiselle Renstrom   Moiselle Renstrom

Happily and smoothly

1. Like snow - y feath - ers in the air White
2. The hill is steep; we hur - ry so, Our

fair - ies come a - rid-ing; They cov - er up the
cheeks grow red and ros - y; When dark-ness comes, in-

hill so bare; Now we may go slid - ing.
side we'll go, Where it's warm and co - zy.

Two Little Valentines

Moiselle Renstrom   Moiselle Renstrom

One lit - tle val - en - tine and then one more!

I'll make them and slip them un-der-neath your door.

Two lit - tle val - en - tines are on their way

To show that I think of you on Val-en-tine's Day.

Ethel Crowninshield

Ethel Crowninshield

With vigor

I'm the po-lice-man who stands on the cor - ner,

Watch - ing the traf - fic go by.

I put up my hand and all of the driv - ers

Stop! or I have to know why.

Song of the Wind

Ethel Crowninshield

Yugoslavian Folk Tune

Tenderly

1ST CHOIR 1. "Wind soft - ly blow - ing,
2D CHOIR 2. "I am a rov - er,

Oh, where are you go - ing?
I search the world o - ver;

And where do you come from
Oh, I am the trav - 'ler

As ev - er you roam?"
Who nev - er goes home."

Trading

Beatrice Wadhams

Mary B. Black

Quietly but not too slow

1ST VOICE 1. "May I buy your Ted - dy bear,
2. "You may have my duck called 'Fluff'
2D VOICE 3. "Thank you for your duck called 'Fluff.'

With his yel - low and curl - y hair?
If the sol - dier is not e - nough;
Sure - ly this will be quite e - nough.

If I may, I'll trade with you
In the tub the duck will swim;
You may have my Ted - dy bear

My lit - tle sol - dier paint - ed blue.
I think it ver - y brave of him."
Aft - er I've brushed his curl - y hair."

1

Seeing

Reproduced by permission, from the painting
by the American artist JESSIE WILLCOX SMITH

Seeing

Richard Gage

French Folk Tune

Gracefully

1. Kneel - ing down be - side the pool,
2. Look - ing at my pic - ture there,

With the eve-ning shad-ows soft - ly creep-ing,
I can see my face so clear - ly show-ing;

I can see the moon come peep - ing
I can see the breez - es blow-ing

In be - tween the trees all green and cool.
Two white rib-bons that are on my hair.

1

Big Bear and Little Bear

Lucy K. Milburn

Newton Swift

Playfully

1ST CHOIR 1. Big Bear and Lit - tle Bear sat in the wood,
ALL   2. Lit - tle Bear was not so good as you think;

And Big Bear said, "Now I hope you'll be good.
He climbed that tree just as quick as a wink.

Stay where you are! You must not fol - low me
Buzz - ing and sting - ing the bees flew a - round,

While I get some hon-ey for you from the tree!"
And Lit - tle Bear fell all the way to the ground.

The Coming of Spring

Ethel H. Tewksbury

R. T. Bjorkman

Happily

1. Soon red will be the ma - ple tree,
2. The flow'rs will know 'tis time to grow;

And grass will start a - peep - ing;
The buds will soon be show - ing;

And then, some day, the puss - ies gray
The birds will sing be - cause 'tis spring,

Will wak - en from their sleep - ing.
With breez - es soft - ly blow - ing.

Pussy Willow

Elizabeth Garrett

Swedish Folk Tune

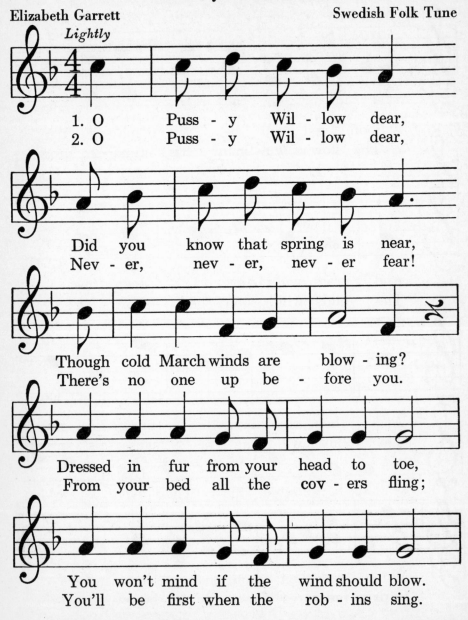

Lightly

1. O Puss - y Wil - low dear,
2. O Puss - y Wil - low dear,

Did you know that spring is near,
Nev - er, nev - er, nev - er fear!

Though cold March winds are blow - ing?
There's no one up be - fore you.

Dressed in fur from your head to toe,
From your bed all the cov - ers fling;

You won't mind if the wind should blow.
You'll be first when the rob - ins sing.

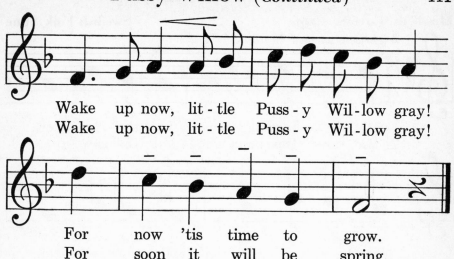

Wake up now, lit - tle Puss - y Wil - low gray!
Wake up now, lit - tle Puss - y Wil - low gray!

For now 'tis time to grow.
For soon it will be spring.

Beetles

Monica Shannon

Mary Root Kern

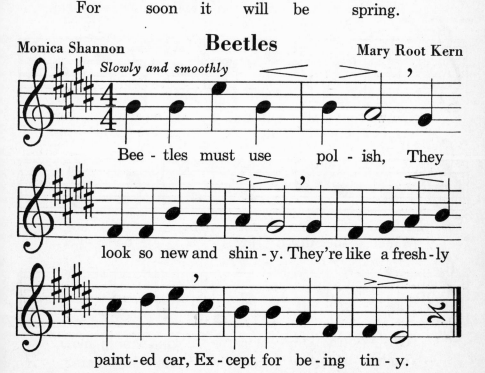

Slowly and smoothly

Bee - tles must use pol - ish, They look so new and shin - y. They're like a fresh - ly paint - ed car, Ex - cept for be - ing tin - y.

The Clover Field

Marchette Gaylord Chute   Swedish Folk Tune

1. Oh, we've been play-ing in the clo-ver,
2. See, it's the men who did the sow-ing

Roll-ing o-ver in the clo-ver.
Who are go-ing to the mow-ing,

Now that the sum-mer's al-most o-ver,
Out where the clo-ver tops are grow-ing.

It is time for the mow-ing.
When the mow-ing is o-ver,

We'll watch the mow-ing.
We'll rake the clo-ver.

Early Easter Bunny (*Continued*)

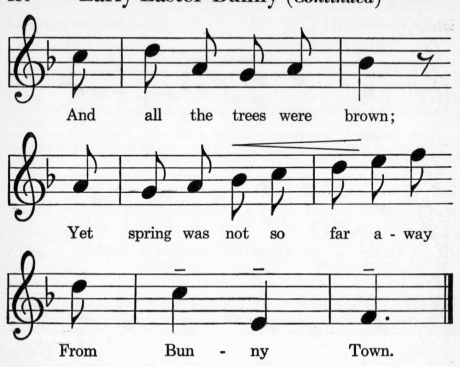

And all the trees were brown;

Yet spring was not so far a-way

From Bun-ny Town.

Beautiful Spring

Mabel Caroline Bjornstad   Mabel Caroline Bjornstad

2D Choir   Do you know why the but-ter-flies, birds, and bees,

1st Choir   And why the green leaves that are   on   the trees

Have   come   a - gain   for   you   and   me?

ALL   Why,   beau - ti - ful spring is   here,   you see.

Fox and Goose

English version by
Beatrice Wadhams

Swedish Folk Song

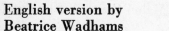

Merrily

1. Fox sit - ting on a chair, on a chair,
2. Fox wait - ing for a goose, for a goose,

Tag me, Fox - y Mis - ter!
You won't find an - oth - er;

You are clev - er, but you nev - er
Fox - y wink - ing, fox - y blink - ing,

Catch me or my sis - ter!
Will you catch my broth - er?

Ragman

William Bowers

Haswell Van Horn

Here comes a fun - ny old, rag - ged old man,

Walk-ing a - long as fast as he can,

Call - ing, call - ing, "Bot - tles and rags!

All kinds of rub - bish to put in my bags."

Little Bow-wow and Little Meow

Moiselle Renstrom   Moiselle Renstrom

ALL   Lit - tle Bow - wow and   lit - tle Me - ow

Met   on   a   sum - mer's   day; · ·

1st Choir Said lit - tle Bow-wow to   lit - tle Me - ow,

"You'd bet - ter   run   a - way; · ·

Or   I   may chase and   fright-en you now."

2D CHOIR "Oh,   is   that so!" said   lit - tle Me - ow;

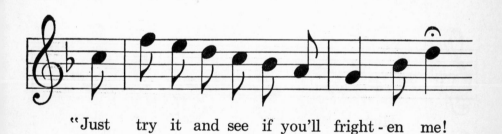

"Just   try it and see if you'll fright - en   me!

For   I'll   jump up   and   sit   in a tree."

Jumping Rope

Elizabeth C. Taylor   C. D. Daniel

With vigor

1st Voice 1. "Will you please jump with me? · ·
2d Voice 2. "Yes, I will jump with you, · ·

It's   fun,   as   you   will   see; · ·
If   you would like   me   to; · ·

High   or   low,   fast   or   slow,
In   and   out,   turn   a - bout;

Turn   the   rope, one,   two,   three." ·
I   like   to   jump   with   you." ·

The Farmyard

Lois Lenski

Swedish Folk Tune

Not too fast

1. The horse is al - ways neigh - ing;
2. The hens are al - ways cack - ling;
3. I love to sing and whis - tle;

The sheep say, "Baa!" the whole day through;
The roost - ers cock - a - doo - dle - doo!
My tunes are pret - ty as can be;

The pigs are al - ways squeal - ing;
The ducks from dawn to sun - set
But through the farm - yard nois - es

The cow says, "Moo!"
Are quack - ing, too!
No one hears me!

The Holiday

Marjorie Knapp

Swedish Folk Tune

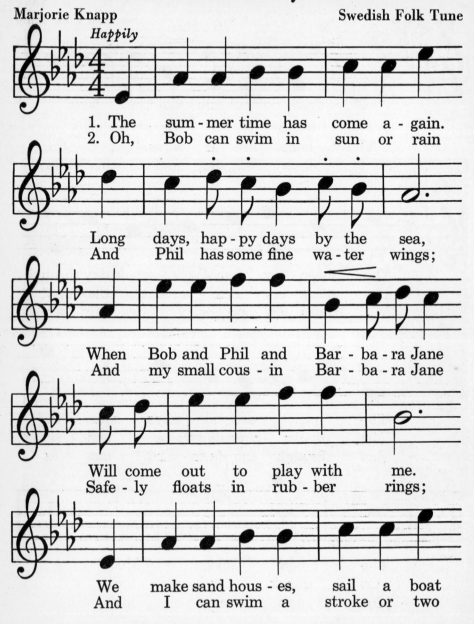

Happily

1. The sum - mer time has come a - gain.
2. Oh, Bob can swim in sun or rain

Long days, hap - py days by the sea,
And Phil has some fine wa - ter wings;

When Bob and Phil and Bar - ba - ra Jane
And my small cous - in Bar - ba - ra Jane

Will come out to play with me.
Safe - ly floats in rub - ber rings;

We make sand hous - es, sail a boat
And I can swim a stroke or two

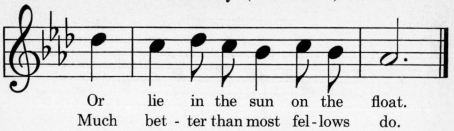

Or lie in the sun on the float.
Much bet - ter than most fel - lows do.

The Art Extension Press, Inc.

The Holiday

Painted by the American artist EDWARD HENRY POTTHAST.
It is now in the Art Institute at Chicago, Illinois

The Weather Man

Kathleen Malone

English Folk Tune

Happily

The weath - er man, the weath - er man,

He does the ver - y best he can;

And wheth - er the weath-er be dark or clear,

We al - ways have a jol - ly time here.

Looking Up and Down

Gretchen O. Murray

Newton Swift

Quietly but not too slow

1. When I look up and see the sky,
2. High would I go a - bove the trees,

Where o - ver - head the clouds go by,
Fly - ing up - on the sum - mer breeze,

Birds fly - ing up and up so high
See - ing be - low the things I please.

Make me feel like fly - ing, too.
What a love - ly thing to do!

1

Robin, Robin

Hope Ann Rhodes

Polish Folk Tune

Joyously

1ST CHOIR
1. Rob - in, Rob - in looks so mer - ry,
2. I can hear the ba - bies call - ing,

2D CHOIR
In her bill a fine red cher - ry
From the nest they're al - most fall - ing;

1ST CHOIR
For her ba - bies who are grow - ing.
Such a fun - ny noise they're mak - ing,

Ev - 'ry day I see her go - ing,
What a din - ner they are tak - ing!

ALL
Tak - ing to her chil - dren three
Ev - 'ry bill is o - pen wide

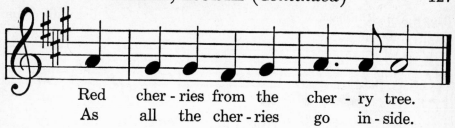

Red cher - ries from the cher - ry tree.
As all the cher - ries go in - side.

The Fire Engine

Ethel Crowninshield   Ethel Crowninshield

With spirit

1st Choir   Too! too! too!   Hear the whis-tle blow-ing!

2d Choir   Ding! ding! ding!   See the en-gine go - ing

All   Round the cor - ner   out of sight,

Ev - er read - y day or night.

The Sheep

Translated by
Cecil Cowdrey

Swiss Folk Song

With spirit

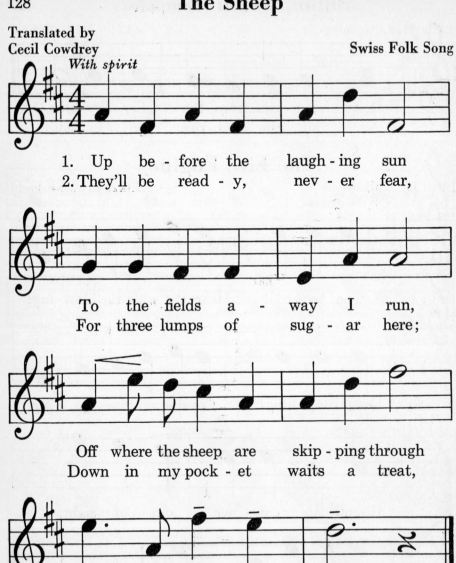

1. Up be - fore the laugh - ing sun
2. They'll be read - y, nev - er fear,

To the fields a - way I run,
For three lumps of sug - ar here;

Off where the sheep are skip - ping through
Down in my pock - et waits a treat,

Grass - es wet with dew.
Sug - ar fine and sweet.

Lolia M. Littlehales Lolia M. Littlehales

In swaying rhythm

Step light - ly, bow - ing left and right;

Step light - ly, 'tis a pret - ty sight; Danc - ing the

love - ly min - u - et Of long a - go.

A Long Time Ago

Ann Anthony

Polish Folk Tune

1. Long a - go, says grand - m'a,
2. Lamps were used for light - ing,

There was no ra - di - o;
There was no oth - er way;

There were no au - to - mo - biles,
I'm sure I like it bet - ter

No signs with "Stop" and "Go."
To be a - live to - day!

Polliwog

Elizabeth C. Taylor

C. D. Daniel

With expression

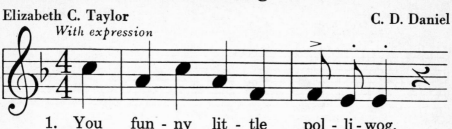

1. You   fun - ny   lit - tle   pol - li - wog,
2. You'll   wear   a   love - ly   spot - ted coat,

Some   day you'll change in - to   a   frog,
And   some-where deep down   in your throat

And   then   up - on   a   moss - y   log
You'll   find   a   grown - up   frog - gy   note,

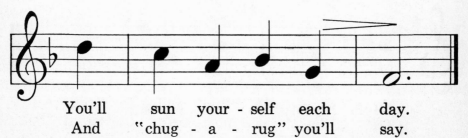

You'll   sun   your - self   each   day.
And   "chug - a - rug" you'll   say.

The Woodpecker

Minnie Loenholdt   Minnie Loenholdt

1. A wood-peck - er pecked a   hole in a tree.
2. The   time passed a-way, when high in the tree,

"Rap,   rap!" said he, "Tap,   tap!" said he.
"Rap,   rap!" said he, "Tap,   tap!" said he.

"I'll   try my best to   build me   a nest,
"I'll   feed my ti - ny   wood-peck-ers three.

Rap,   rap, tap,   tap!" said   he.
Rap,   rap, tap,   tap!" said   he.

Night and Morning

Marchette Gaylord Chute

C. D. Daniel

In graceful rhythm

Softly 1. When I have gone to bed, · ·
Brightly 2. When morn - ing comes a - gain, · ·

The moon comes up to say: · ·
The sun says with a smile, · ·

"Go to sleep, go to sleep,
"Hur - ry up! Hur - ry up!

Go to sleep right a - way." · ·
Come out - doors for a while!" · ·

A Ride

Mildred Adair   Mildred Adair

2D CHOIR Toot, toot, toot!   Here   is   the train.

Honk, honk, honk!   Here   is   the   car.

1ST CHOIR Whir, whir, whir!   Here   is   the plane. ·

Where should you like to ride?   I'll   take the train.
(car)
(plane)

The Sandman

Mary Smith

Austrian Folk Tune

Lightly and smoothly

1. Tap - ping soft - ly at
2. 'Tis the sand - man come

some - bod - y's door, Tap - ping at
down from the skies, Throw - ing his

some - bod - y's door, Who can it
sleep in your eyes. He will not

be? We will o - pen and see.
stay But will hur - ry a - way.

Child's Prayer

Marjorie Knapp

Robert Schumann

1. The hours of dark are past;
2. In sun-shine or in rain,

The sun-shine comes at last.
Till eve-ning comes a-gain,

We thank Thee for the qui-et night;
Both while we work and while we play,

We thank Thee for the light.
Be with us all the day.

Hymn of Thanks

Marjorie Knapp

Robert Jackson

1. As sing - ing birds bring praise
2. We thank Thee for our friends,

Through notes of hap - py song,
For all our mer - ry hours,

So would we bring our thanks to Thee,
Our games and plays and sto - ry books,

To Whom · we all be - long.
Our gar - den bright with flow'rs.

America

S. F. Smith

Henry Carey

With spirit

1. My coun - try! 'tis of thee, Sweet land of
2. My na - tive coun - try, thee, Land of the
3. Let mu - sic swell the breeze, And ring from
4. Our fa - thers' God! to Thee, Au - thor of

lib - er - ty, Of thee I sing; Land where my
no - ble free, Thy name I love; I love thy
all the trees Sweet free-dom's song; Let mor - tal
lib - er - ty, To Thee we sing; Long may our

fa - thers died, Land of the Pil - grims' pride!
rocks and rills, Thy woods and tem - pled hills;
tongues a - wake, Let all that breathe par - take,
land be bright With free - dom's ho - ly light!

From ev - 'ry moun - tain side Let free - dom ring.
My heart with rap - ture thrills Like that a - bove.
Let rocks their si - lence break, The sound pro - long.
Pro - tect us by Thy might, Great God, our King!

Alphabetical Index

139